W9-CTD-066

apeiron ragazzi 3

Original title: Colosseo. La storia di un gladiatore.
Apeiron Editori, Sant'Oreste (Rome), 2008

Translation: Amina Santcross

Design and lay-out: Maria Korporal
www.mariakorporal.com

Printed by Arti Grafiche La Moderna S.n.c.
Via Enrico Fermi 13/17
00012 Guidonia M. RM – Italy

ISBN 9788885978645
First edition, Sant'Oreste (Roma), 2008
Second edition, Sant'Oreste (Roma), 2014
Third edition, Sant'Oreste (Roma), 2016

© Apeiron Editori S.n.c.
Località Pantano
00060 Sant'Oreste RM – Italy

www.apeironeditori.com

The COLOSSEUM
The story of a gladiator

Written by Valerio Sailis
Illustrated by Paola Canzonetta

ΑΠΕΙΡΟΝ
APEIRON

Hello, dear children everywhere! Let me introduce myself. My name is Anassa, which in Greek means queen. However, don't be deceived by my name because, even though I have a foreign name, I am a true Roman. My mother called me Anassa to please my father Aetos, who was born in Athens, the capital of Greece, about two thousand years ago.

Do you know how old I am? I am more than 1950 years old! Yes, I know, I am rather old, I have a few aches and pains and wear glasses to help me see better, but when I was young I was a most beautiful eagle with blue eyes and feathers the colour of the moon. I was so beautiful that one day a Roman emperor, seeing me fly in the Roman skies, fell in love with me and gave me the title of Imperial Eagle.

I was born in October 54 A.D. To tell you the truth, I am not very pleased about the month and year of my birth. Do you know why? Because Nero was proclaimed Emperor on that date. I didn't like Nero, as I don't like all those who enjoy playing with fire. Playing with fire is dangerous! Anyway, children, the Rome of today is very different from Imperial Rome. At that time, there wasn't the chaos caused by cars, there was not even McDonald's; children didn't play with Play Station, and didn't watch the Disney Channel… but, wait a minute! Do I hear some of you giggling? Are you making fun of me? All right, if you don't believe me, go and ask my dearest friend, the goose. Her name is Anser and she lives on the hill where the town hall is. The mayor had a house

TO ANSER, THE MOST AUDACIOUS GOOSE IN THE CAPITOL, WHOSE COURAGE SAVED US FROM BEING ATTACKED BY THE GAULS.

built specially for her right under the statue of Marcus Aurelius, and ordered that above the door there should be a marble plaque bearing the inscription: "To Anser, the most audacious Goose in the Capitol, whose courage saved us from being attacked by the Gauls." If you don't believe me, go and speak to her on her entry phone and ask her if I'm not telling the truth! In the meantime I will begin to tell you the eventful story of a gladiator. In fact, "the Gladiator!" The most famous of all those who fought in the Colosseum! Before I start, however, it may be a good idea to brush off the dust from a page of history. For example, do you know what the Colosseum is? Of course, you do, but do you know why it was built and how tall it is? Do you know that there was a "velarium"? Do you know what a "velarium" is?

"Wait, wait. Anassa, you're asking too many questions, too quickly!" I seem to hear someone saying. You are right; I do ask too many questions. Now, however, we will begin at the beginning and I will tell you the story of the Colosseum.

The Colosseum, once known as the Flavian Amphitheatre, or simply "amphitheatre" as the Romans, at that time, used to call it, was started by the Emperor Vespasian, a member of the Flavian dynasty, between 70 and 72 A.D. It was completed about 10 years later, in A.D.80, under the Emperor Titus. He gifted it to the people to make himself more popular, seeing that the majority of the people wanted only two things, "panem et cir-

AMPHITHEATRUM
FLAVIUM

censes", which means, to have a full stomach and to enjoy the games in the circus!

Work started on a site just east of the Roman Forum, exactly where the famous gardens surrounding Nero's "Domus Aurea" (Golden House) were situated, and where there used to be a colossal statue of Nero, from which the Colosseum takes its name. Oh! For those who may not know it, the Forum was a big market place.

The Colosseum has an oval shape with a circumference of 527 metres. Do you know what oval means? It means shaped like an egg. Let's do an experiment. Take an egg and, using a pin, make a small hole at each end of the egg. Next, blow very hard in one of the holes to allow the inside to empty. Next, try to cut the shell in half, throw away the

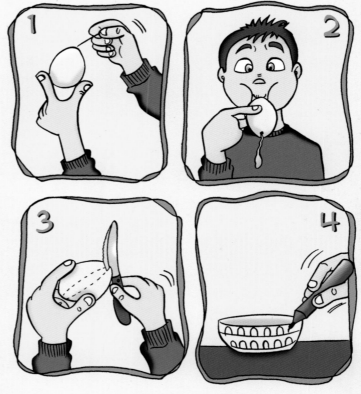

upper part, place the base on the kitchen table and with a small paintbrush draw several small arches. There you have it. You have built your own Colosseum!

Where were we? Oh, yes! I was saying that the Colosseum has an oval shape. Originally it was 52 metres tall, whereas today it is 48 and half metres. Over 100 thousand cubic metres of travertine stone were used for the building which consists of four floors. The first three have 80 arcades each, also known as "fornici" (barrel arches). The upper floor has a plain wall with 40 windows, above which were positioned the poles which allowed for the opening

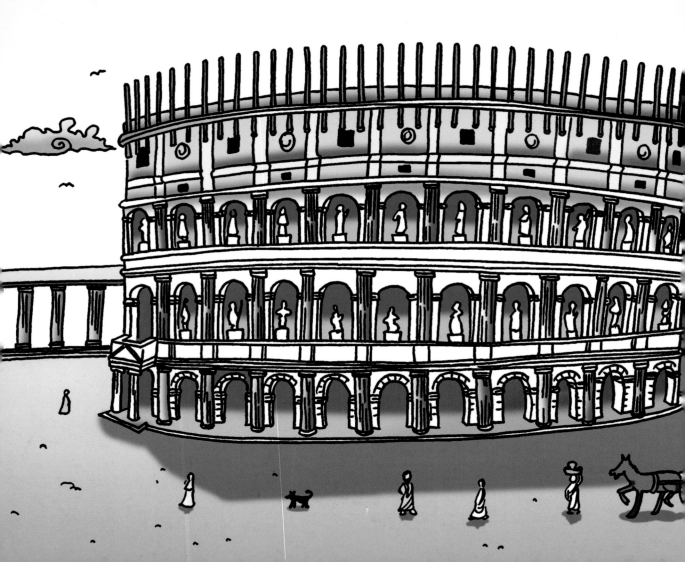

and closing of the "velarium". The "velarium" was a kind of large awning that protected the spectators from the hot sun or from the rain. The amphitheatre could hold at least 50 thousand spectators. Everyone had a numbered seat depending on his or her status. For example, the seats on the top floor, judged as the worst, were reserved for women. Those on the lowest floor, deemed as the best, were reserved for the senators. Here was also the emperor's seat known as the "pulvinar". Beneath the arena there were chambers and passages where wild beasts and gladiators were kept before the start of the games.

The gladiators were usually slaves, prisoners of war or men condemned to death. But there were also those who chose to become gladiators attracted by the fame and glory that the games could bring them! Usually, the "ludi", (the fights between gladiators) took place between two different categories of fighters. The standard pairing facing each other consisted of a retiarius and a mirmillon. The duel ended, almost always, with the death of one of the two contenders. The loser, however, could ask for mercy from the emperor who would decide to let him live or die.

The story I am about to tell you happened a long, long time ago, in A.D.176 to be precise. I was 122 years old, then, and therefore still quite young! At that time the emperor of Rome was Marcus Aurelius who was considered to be one of the "five good emperors".

I remember that morning well. It was a most beautiful summer's day. The sky was blue and cloudless and...

The Forum is crowded and noisy. There are priests from the East, sacred dancers, merchants, and slaves. Claudius, a young man, 23 years old, tall, handsome, well-built, full of strength and vigour, carries his three-year-old son, Martius on his shoulders. Beside him walks his wife Berenice, a most beautiful young woman, with long golden hair, beautiful as no other in the world!

At a certain moment the crowd parts to make way for a "biga" (a two horsed chariot) with three young men aboard and escorted by ten or twelve centurions. The driver is Commodus, the son of the Emperor Marcus Aurelius. He is a cruel young man who prefers to spend his time in the gym rather than studying. He also likes, every now and then, to go to the forum to look for beautiful young slaves to buy and take back to his palace. Commodus pulls on the reins and the biga stops.

"I want that one!" he says, pointing an outstretched arm at the beautiful young woman with the long golden hair. At this, two centurions dismount from their horses and seize the young woman by the arms.

Claudius, her husband, sets his little boy down on the ground and shouts, "Stop! Let go of my wife!" Then in no time at all, he throws himself at the two and starts kicking and punching them.

Seeing Claudius giving his soldiers a good beating, Commodus remains silent. Then all of a sudden he bursts out laughing and exclaims, "Eros!"

A year before he met Berenice, Claudius was still a gladiator. He was neither a slave, nor a prisoner. He was a free man and had decided to attend a school for gladiators. He had chosen the best, called the "Ludus Magnus". There he had signed a contract which obliged him to fight always to the death. However, he had not decided to become a gladiator for the excitement or for the glory he might achieve. He had a noble reason for his action. He hoped to earn 10 thousand sesterces (about 20 thousand euros) to buy the freedom of one of his friends.

Life at the school was hard and his "lanista", that is, his trainer, was a hard taskmaster. Claudius, however, trained from morning to evening without ever complaining. He became famous throughout Rome soon after his first fights. He was exceptionally strong, but also intelligent and graceful. He used to fight with courage and dignity. If by chance he was wounded in an arm or a leg, he would not cry out or wince with pain; the expression on his face remained unchanged!

He fought as a retiarius. The retiarii carried a trident and a net to capture their opponents. They fought naked except for a loincloth around the waist and a bronze left shoulder guard. They had no leg protections, did not carry a shield and did not hide their faces behind a helmet. Claudius did not mind; he was proud to show his face to the public. He was very popular in Rome, especially among the women. He had an athlete's body and all the young girls were in love with him. They called him Eros, the god of love, and would write messages on the city walls such as, "Eros, puellarum dominus", which means "Eros, the god of young women". The men called him "magnanimus" which means

generous, because at the end of each victorious fight, he would ask for the life of his adversary to be spared. If the emperor gave the thumbs up sign, the loser would live, if, however, he gave the thumbs down sign, that is "verso", Claudius would have to kill him.

Within a year, Claudius fought 30 fights and won them all. Usually most of the money would go to the "lanistae", but it was different for Eros because he would get half of the agreed prize money

for each fight, and consequently, he earned an enormous amount of money, almost 200 thousand sesterces, the equivalent of 400 thousand euros! However, he did not keep the money for himself because he thought of it as blood money! He chose, instead, to use it for charitable works; it is said that he helped more than a thousand poor families to live a better life. He took just enough money to buy the freedom of his friend and then decided to stop fighting, because he hated to kill and shed innocent blood.

The Roman people were disappointed. They thought that he was the best gladiator of them all and could not bear the thought of not seeing him fight again. The emperor himself asked him to continue, but he refused. Marcus Aurelius, who was a good man, understood the feelings of the young warrior and did not insist. At the end of that very year, Claudius met Berenice. They fell in love and married. They decided to move to Fidene, a small town on the outskirts of Rome, where they bought a piece of land and built their own house. They had a vegetable garden and kept two goats and a dog. Later Berenice gave birth to a son, little Martius.

Eros wished to forget all about his life as a gladiator…

Commodus, seeing Claudius hitting his soldiers, first bursts out laughing and then calls out, "Eros!"

"My name is not Eros! My name is Claudius! Tell your soldiers never again to touch my wife, not even with one finger, or else, I swear, I will kill them," shouts Claudius. Commodus, defiantly, carries on laughing. Then he turns to Claudius and says, "She is not a slave then? She is your wife! But I don't care because I am the emperor's son and every wish is my command. So, if I say that your wife must be my slave, it must be so!" Then the cruel Commodus adds, "You know, Eros, today I feel particularly generous and I want to give you a chance. In a week's time it will be my birthday, and for the occasion, my father, the emperor, has decided to hold the games in the circus. And you…"

Meanwhile, all the centurions have dismounted from their horses to replace some of those who Claudius has struck down. Two of them guard Berenice, and another has Martius in his arms. The little boy kicks and punches the soldier, while five or seven centurions hold Claudius who is listening to what Commodus is saying.

"There will be many festivities for my birthday. If you want your wife back you will have to fight against ten opponents and you must defeat them all. Otherwise you will die and your beautiful little wife will become my slave. As for your son, well, he will make a tasty morsel for the lions and the tigers. Ha, ha, ha!"

Commodus then orders his soldiers to arrest the family, including the little boy. The soldiers tie Berenice's hands behind her back and lift her onto a horse. Little Martius is still in the centurion's arms, but continues to kick and punch the soldier, who does not know how to restrain him. Meanwhile, Claudius, in order to protect his wife and son from further suffering, allows the soldiers to chain his hands and feet.

Those witnessing the scene are dismayed and upset. When the group of soldiers and their prisoners walk away some-one mutters, "If Commodus had not been the son of the emperor, Claudius would have enjoyed ripping his heart out with his bare hands.

Commodus, you're such a coward!" Others curse him, "Commodus, you're a wicked man! May the gods punish you!" However, even though the people are upset, they are also beginning to feel a kind of excitement at the thought of seeing Eros fight again in the Colosseum.

The news spreads like wildfire.

The next day, the city walls are covered with notices proclaiming:

I, COMMODUS, SON OF CAESAR MARCUS AURELIUS ANTONINUS AUGUSTUS IMPERATOR, ANNOUNCE THAT ON THE 21ST OF AUGUST, TO CELEBRATE MY SIXTEENTH BIRTHDAY, THE GLADIATORIAL GAMES WILL BE HELD IN THE COLOSSEUM. AND TO SHOW ME GREATER HONOUR, EROS WILL MAKE HIS COMEBACK AND WILL FIGHT AGAINST ASTEROPAEUS, HILARUS, ATTILIO, INCITATUS, CELADUS, SATORNILUS, CRESCES, DIODORO, URBICO AND ERMES.

They are the names of the ten best and strongest gladiators in the world, known to be unbeatable. It seems truly an impossible task, especially because usually a gladiator undertook only two or three fights in a year. Claudius, however, will have to defeat ten opponents in a single day!
It really seems an impossible test!

Claudius spends the following days training. He even trains at night. He must not fail. Were he to lose even one duel, it would mean the end of what he holds most dear in the world, his wife and his son. He must not fail!

The long awaited day has arrived. The people are excited and pour into the streets already before daylight. Some queue outside the Colosseum hours before the start of the games. Soon the amphitheatre is full with 50 thousand excited spectators.

The programme starts with the fights between animals, followed, at lunchtime, by the executions of criminals, the athletic contests and the comic acts. Finally it is early afternoon, time for the main attraction of the day. It is time for the mighty Eros to prove himself against the strongest gladiators in the world. The atmosphere is feverish. The spectators go wild. They stand up, shout, and clap.

The gladiators enter the arena accompanied by a group of musicians. They approach the "pulvinar", the seat of the emperor, occupied today by Commodus, and salute him, "Ave, Commode, morituri te salutant." (Hail Commodus, those who are about to die, salute you.)

Meanwhile, Claudius, who is still in one of the underground passages, prays to the gods that they may give him strength to face his opponents. His moment has now arrived. He is made to go into a cage which is raised up very slowly. As the cage rises up, Claudius sees that the arena is full. When the cage is level with the ground, its door is opened and out steps the real hero of the day, a most handsome warrior, dressed in a red robe adorned with gold. At first, Claudius, stands still, transfixed by the spectacle. It brings back bad memories and events which he had wished to forget and never experience again. Instead, he is here again because he has to; in the past it was for his friend's freedom, today it is for the life of his family. He starts to walk. The spectators seem spellbound. They have stopped shouting.

All around the arena there is an incredible silence. They are all dazzled by this handsome man who they see walking with courage and determination. Claudius is now in the centre of the arena. He stops. Silence. Then, suddenly, a woman, seated on the upper section of the arena shouts, "Hail Eros!" The cry seems to wake up the spectators. In no time, all 50 thousand of them echo her greeting, "Hail Eros! Hail, Eros!" They resume their clapping and shout even more excitedly than before. The noise is deafening.

Two slaves approach Claudius and remove his red robe. Being a retiarius, Claudius wears only a loincloth, and a bronze left shoulder guard which reaches to his elbow. They hand him a trident and a net. Everything is ready; the great Eros has returned!

Commodus orders the games to start. Claudius waits while the ten gladiators draw lots. His first opponent is a mirmillon. He wears a fish-like helmet and protection on his left leg, on his wrists, and on his elbows. He holds a big oval shield and a sword.

The two fighters stand face to face. The referee arrives and checks the weapons.

The two study one another; it looks as if neither of them wants to make the first move. The public continues to shout. Then Eros raises his trident and makes a sudden movement with his left arm.

The mirmillon, believing that he is about to be stabbed, tries to avoid the expected blow, but, in so doing, he receives a mighty kick right on his bottom. The spectators burst out laughing; in fact they roar with laughter.

Offended by being made a fool of, the mirmillon, first shouts with rage, then tries repeatedly to run his opponent through with his sword. However, his blows come to nothing because Claudius dodges them all with amazing speed. The duel continues until the crowd's favourite whirls his net in the air and throws it at the mirmillon, who trips, loses his balance, falls to the ground and ends up caught in the net like a fish.

Eros approaches his prey and places a foot on the man's right shoulder. The defeated gladiator pleads for mercy by lifting his left index finger.

The public shouts, "Verbera!" (hit him). Then, "Iugula!" (cut his throat).

Commodus, however, ignores the people's wishes. He stands up and gives the thumbs up sign, and in so doing saves the mirmillon's life. The people, all 50 thousand of them, are furious and whistle in disapproval.

33

At the end of the second fight, won again by Eros, Commodus, confronted by the defeated gladiator begging for mercy, shows the thumbs down sign (verso) and so Eros kills him. Next to enter the arena is a slave disguised as Charon. (Charon is the ferryman of the dead. His task is to ferry the souls of the deceased across the river Styx). He carries a hot iron with which he checks that the defeated gladiator is really dead, and then other slaves thrust a hook into the man's flesh and drag him away.

The third encounter now starts. Eros continues to fight with great concentration trusting also in the help of the gods. He wins this duel too. Then he wins the fourth, the fifth and all the others, including the last. He is exhausted, but happy! Of course, he is also sad because he has been forced to kill five men because Commodus, just as he had done at the end of the first two fights, has shown mercy to one loser, and condemned to death the loser of the subsequent encounter. Eros, however, is happy because he can be reunited with his family, so he walks towards the imperial seat and, when he is under the "pulvinar", asks Commodus to free his wife and son. But, as we know, Commodus is truly a cruel

man and says, "Well done, Claudius, you have fought well – maybe too well for my liking. Everybody here knows that you are the strongest gladiator and few would bet on you being defeated. To tell you the truth, I was already yawning from the fourth or fifth fight onwards because I knew how it would all end, that is, that you would win. Alas, I got bored. Now, therefore, I really want to enjoy myself!"

At this he orders a cage to be hoisted up. Eros and the public look puzzled towards the gate of the underground passage, which, on opening, enables the wild animals to enter the arena. Suddenly a lion's head appears. The cage is opened. The beast takes a few steps and then stops. All around the arena people gasp, "Oh! Oh!" It is a gigantic beast; they have never seen such a huge lion. It is almost as big as an elephant! Eros can't believe his eyes. For the first time in his life he is almost petrified with terror, and only just manages to bend down to pick up his sword.

The enormous beast, as soon as its sight has adjusted to the sunlight, which at first had blinded it, becomes aware of its opponent. It quickly eyes Eros and runs towards him. Eros takes up a defensive position, as far as it is possible for him to defend himself against such a monster, and almost fails to notice when the lion, with the claws of one of its paws, hits his left arm and almost wrenches it from his shoulder. Eros, his arm bleeding, almost faints with pain, but he holds on. He does not cry out, nor does he complain. The only sign of his suffering is a pained expression on his face. The lion turns and starts to walk away; it seems as if it has lost interest in the man, but after a few steps, turns round again, and gives such a mighty roar that the crowd is terrified. Then it starts running again and this time it jumps on top of Eros who falls to the ground, buried under the enormous animal. It looks as if the great warrior has been swallowed up by the underworld; there remains no trace of him. The people can't believe their eyes. They are on their feet. Some pull at their hair. Others shake their heads. The women cry.

Eros is dead. Silence! Silence descends on the arena.

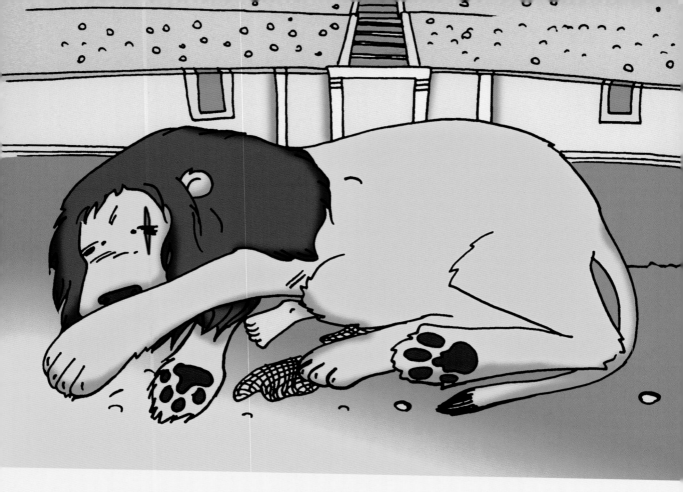

At a certain moment, however, announced by a flourish of trumpets, Marcus Aurelius, the emperor, appears on the "pulvinar", the imperial seat. He has just returned to Rome, having defeated the Germans and the Sarmatians during the Marcomannic wars, and as soon as he has been told that the "ludi", the gladiatorial games, organised by Commodus, are taking place in the Colosseum, has quickly made his way there.

His eyes fall on a frightful scene: an enormous animal is stretched out on the ground and from under its great frame a man's foot sticks out. The emperor knows well whose foot that is.

"This time you have surpassed yourself, Commodus! Your behaviour dishonours my name!" He looks angrily at his son, and almost hits him, but then restrains himself and orders, "Free that man, wash him, anoint his body with unguents, dress him in red and decorate him with gold. Let him be buried with the honours paid only to great heroes!"

Twenty slaves enter the arena and, before approaching the monster, throw a few stones at him. The lion remains still. It, too, seems dead, but is this possible? The slaves start to push it to make it roll on his side, so that they can free Eros's body. As soon as they manage to move the heavy beast, they stand back amazed.

An instant before being crushed by the lion's body, Eros, without anybody realising it, had time to strike it with his sword, slitting the lion from its stomach to its throat.
This means that Eros could still be...

"HE IS ALIVE! HE IS ALIVE! I hear him breathe!" One of the slaves screams.

The people start to shout again with happiness, and to applaud wildly. Among the senators is also seated Galenus, Marcus Aurelius's personal doctor. He runs to the scene and checks the state of Eros's health. The gladiator has several fractured ribs, caused by the lion's weight, and an arm torn by the beast's claws, but he is alive!

Eros is carried on a stretcher out of the arena, to the applause and cries of joy from the crowd.

A man shouts, "Cruel Commodus! Cruel Commodus! He nearly had him killed! He wasn't satisfied with having seen him fight against ten gladiators!" Soon all 50 thousand spectators shout in unison, "Cruel Commodus! Cruel Commodus!" Then they shout more insults; the noise is deafening. The emperor looks almost in disgust at his son and says, "This is what you deserve: the people's insults!" At this he turns his back on his son and walks away. Commodus remains seated. He watches his father leave and, burning with hatred, mutters, "Father, one day I will kill you!"

Eros, helped by his wife and little son, was taken care of in the emperor's palace. As soon as he regained his strength, the three of them returned to their home in Fidene.

The years that followed were happy ones. They saw their family grow with the birth of Julia, a little sister for Martius, who enjoyed teasing her. Eros lived a peaceful and happy life, well removed from the painful circumstances that had forced him to become a gladiator and kill other men. He died an old man, in his own bed. He had the satisfaction of having lived all his life beside the woman he loved and to have seen his children have their own families, and also to have enjoyed his grandchildren. He asked that on his tombstone should be written, "Here lies Claudius, a free man!"

Well, children! Did you enjoy this story? And to think that I was there. I was perched on a windowsill in the top section of the Colosseum and I can still hear the people's cries of happiness, "Eros is alive! Eros is alive!"
Oh! I feel very emotional when I think of that day. I feel like crying again!

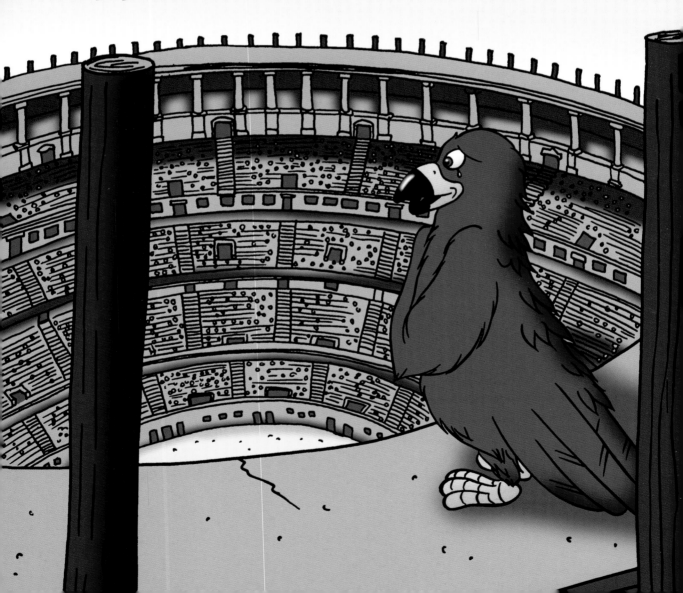

BOOM! Did you hear that gunshot? Don't be afraid, the war hasn't started again! It's the cannon on the Janiculum Hill announcing that it is now midday! MIDDAY?! Oh, dear gods! By now I should have already been at Anser's place for lunch!

Do you remember Anser? My friend the goose, who lives on the Capitoline Hill? The one who saved the Romans from the attack of the Gauls and that... ok, ok. That's another story which you will hear from Anser herself another time. Goodbye children, I must fly away immediately, otherwise, if I am late, Anser will be angry with me. Goodbye, Goodbye!

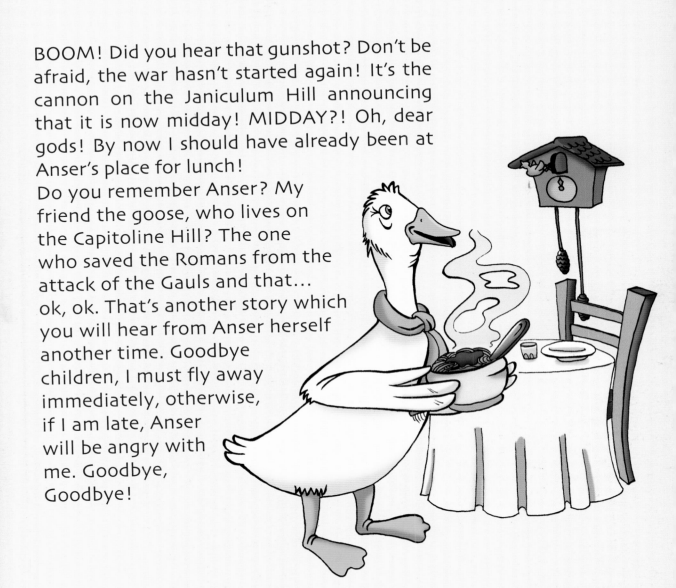

47

already published:

1. Marguerite Yourcenar
   Come Wang-Fô venne salvato

2. Valerio Sailis
   Colosseo. La storia di un gladiatore
3. **The Colosseum. The story of a gladiator**
4. **Coliseo. La historia de un gladiador**
5. **Colisée. L'histoire d'un gladiateur**
6. **Das Kolosseum. Die Geschichte eines Gladiators**
7. **Колизей. История одного гладиатора**
8. **Het Colosseum. Het verhaal van een gladiator**
9. 斗兽场. 一个角斗士的故事

visit our website!

www.apeironeditori.com